Developing Li

PHONICS

PHOTOCOPIABLE ACTIVITIES
FOR THE LITERACY HOUR

book

Christine Moorcroft

A & C BLACK

Contents

Consolidation

Published 2006 by A & C Black Publishers Limited
38 Soho Square, London W1D 3HB
www.acblack.com

ISBN-10: 0-7136-7853-4
ISBN-13: 978-0-7136-7853-6

Copyright text © Christine Moorcroft, 2006
Copyright illustrations © Ana Sáez del Arco, 2006

Editor: Jane Klima
Design: Susan McIntyre

The author and publishers would like to thank Catherine Yemm and Rifat Siddiqui for their assistance in producing this book.

A CIP catalogue record for this book is available from the British Library.

Printed in Great Britain by Caligraving Ltd, Thetford, Norfolk.

This book is produced using paper that is made from wood grown in managed, sustainable forests. It is natural, renewable and recyclable. The logging and manufacturing processes conform to the environmental regulations of the country of origin.

Introduction

Developing Literacy: Phonics is a series of three photocopiable activity books for helping children to recognise and blend phonemes.

Developing Literacy: Word Level provides a good basis for teaching reading and writing through a range of methods, as advocated by the National Literacy Strategy *Framework for Teaching*. **Developing Literacy: Phonics** focuses exclusively on the use of phonics. Teachers should use their professional judgement in selecting the most appropriate activities to develop children's abilities to read and write with confidence.

In response to the promotion by some education consultants and researchers of the exclusive teaching of synthetic phonics, the Secretary of State for Education asked Jim Rose to lead an independent review of the teaching of early reading (see **Useful websites** below). The final report suggested that some teachers might have laid an over-emphasis on word recognition to the detriment of the development of children's understanding of phonics. The review concluded that:

…the case for systematic phonic work is overwhelming and much strengthened by a synthetic approach, the key features of which are to teach beginner readers:

- grapheme/phoneme (letter/sound) correspondences (the alphabetic principle) in a clearly defined, incremental sequence
- to apply the highly important skill of blending (synthesising) phonemes in order, all through a word, to read it
- to apply the skills of segmenting words into their constituent phonemes to spell
- that blending and segmenting are reversible processes.

(Paragraph 51, *Independent review of the teaching of early reading, Final Report*, Jim Rose, March 2006)

Synthetic phonics and Analytic phonics

Synthetic phonics focuses on the pronunciation of the phonemes (sounds) represented by particular graphemes (letters or groups of letters) in isolation and the ways in which these are combined (synthesised), for example, the graphemes *d*, *o* and *g* are combined to form the word *dog*.

Analytic phonics focuses on the ways in which the phonemes represented by particular graphemes are pronounced in specific words, for example, pupils identify the similarity between the words *say*, *sing*, *sit* and *sun* and learn that the initial phoneme is represented by the grapheme *s*.

The activities in **Developing Literacy: Phonics** provide practice in recognising and representing in writing an appropriate range of phonemes, in line with the synthetic phonic approach recommended by the Rose Review. Teachers should use the activity sheets in the order that best matches their school's scheme of work.

Throughout the series the focus is on the phonemes represented by the letters of the alphabet rather than on the names of the letters.

Some of the activities are designed to be carried out with the whole class, some with small groups and some are for individual work. Some are intended for teachers to read aloud to the children and to invite their responses; some are presented in the form of games and other activities and for oral responses; others require a written response.

Each activity sheet features a **Teachers' note** at the foot of the page, which can be masked before photocopying if desired. Expanded teaching notes are provided in the **Notes on the activities** on pages 5–8. Most of the activity sheets end with a challenge (**Now try this!**) which reinforces and extends the children's learning and provides the teacher with an opportunity for assessment. These extension activities might be appropriate for only a few children; it is not expected that the whole class should complete them. On some pages there is space for the children to complete these activities, but others will require a notebook or a separate sheet of paper.

Organisation

The activities require few resources besides pencils, crayons, scissors, glue, word banks and simple dictionaries. Other materials you may need, information books for example, are specified in the **Notes on the activities**.

Reading

Most children will be able to carry out the activities independently. It is not expected that they should be able to read all the instructions on the sheets, but that someone will read them to or with them. Children gradually become accustomed to seeing instructions, and learn their purpose long before they can read them for themselves.

Useful websites

Rose Review final report:
http://www.standards.dfes.gov.uk/rosereview/finalreport/
National Literacy Strategy:
http://www.standards.dfes.gov.uk/primary/literacy/
Sound effects:
http://www.findsounds.com/
http://www.grsites.com/sounds/

Notes on the activities

The notes in this section expand upon those provided at the foot of each activity sheet. They give ideas for making the most of the sheet, including suggestions for a whole-class introduction, the plenary session or for follow-up work using an adapted version of the page. Throughout these activities it is useful to display a pictorial alphabet chart showing the lower-case letters with their upper-case counterparts. It is also helpful to emphasise the consonant and vowel sounds in speech. In some regions the short vowel *a* is lengthened in certain words (for example, *mask*, *grass*, *fast*). Teachers need to be aware of this variation.

Single consonants

These activities focus on phonemes represented by single consonants. They help the children to learn that the same consonant can be used to represent different phonemes, for example, *c* can stand for the soft *s* or the hard *k* sound; *g* can stand for the soft *j* or the hard *g* sound; and *s* can stand for *s* as in *sock* or the *z* sound of *rose*.

Soft c (page 9) is about identifying the soft *c* (*s*) phoneme in speech and recognising when the letter *c* represents this phoneme. The children could first write some words they know that begin with a hard *c*:, *can*, *cat*, *cot*, *crisps*. Say the name of the letter *c*, emphasising the first phoneme. Write *c* on the board and ask the children to say *Soft c says sss*. You could make up 'soft *c*' jingles with the children:

> I have a soft *c* in my *face*;
> You have a soft *c* when you run a *race*.
> There's a soft *c* in every *place*.
> You eat soft *c* in an *ice*;
> Soft *c* tastes very *nice*
> And that's why *mice* eat *rice*.
>
> There's a soft *c* sitting in a *pencil*
> And it's hiding in the *centre* of *stencil*.

Other useful words include: *circle*, *circus*, *dice*, *fence*, *fleece*, *icicle*, *icing*, *lice*, *pace*, *pence*, *police*, *price*, *trace*.

Soft g (page 10) focuses on identifying the soft *g* (*j*) phoneme in speech and recognising when the letter *g* represents this phoneme. The children could first write some words they know that begin with a hard *g*: *gap*, *get*, *go*, *got*, *grab*. Say the name of the letter *g*, emphasising the first phoneme. Write *g* on the board and ask the children to say *Soft g says j*. Other useful words include: *angel*, *change*, *danger*, *genie*, *gentle*, *huge*.

Easy does it and **Lazy daisy** (pages 11–12) develop the ability to identify in speech the *z* phoneme and recognise when it is represented by the letter *s*. Ask the children to spell plural words in which the *s* has a *z* sound: *dogs*, *bibs*, *rugs*, *beds*. Compare the sound represented by *s* in other words ending in *s*, such as *bus*, *bits*, *cups*, *us*. Also discuss examples where *se* represents *z* in words with a split vowel digraph: *nose*, *rise*, *use*, *wise*. Before handing out copies of page 12, give each child a card on which *s* or *z* is written. Ask them to hold up their card when they hear that sound as you read the words.

Double consonants, digraphs and trigraphs

These activities develop the children's understanding that a single consonant phoneme can be represented by more than one letter; that a double letter produces the same sound as a single letter (for example, *rr*); that letters can combine to produce a new sound (for example, *ch*, *th*, *sh*, *ph*, *gh*) and that a letter can be silent (for example, *g*, *k*, *w* in *gnome*, *knife* and *write*). They also learn that the same consonants can stand for different phonemes, for example, *ch* in *each* and *echo*.

This and that (page 13) is about identifying in speech the voiced *th* phoneme. Write up *th* and demonstrate the phoneme it represents in these words. Ensure that the children repeat it correctly (beginning with the tongue between the front teeth and voicing the sound) to produce the voiced *th* sound of *this* rather than the breathed *th* of *thin* (see page 14 notes). Other useful words include: *brother*, *father*, *mother*, *there*, *weather*. Ask the children to make up sentences using voiced *th* words and to read them with a partner.

Thick and thin (page 14) focuses on identifying in speech the breathed *th* phoneme. Write up *th* and demonstrate the phoneme it represents in these words. Ensure that the children repeat it correctly (beginning with the tongue behind the front teeth and breathing the sound) to produce the soft *th* sound of *thick* rather than the harder *th* of *this* (see page 13 notes). Other useful words include: *both*, *moth*, *thirsty*, *throw*, *thump*. Ask the children to make up sentences using breathed *th* words and to read them with a partner.

ph says f (page 15) focuses on identifying and using the *ph* spelling of the *f* phoneme. Write up *ph* and demonstrate the phoneme it represents in words such as *alphabet*, *graph*, *phone*, *photo*. Other useful words include: *elephant*, *nephew*, *orphan*, *phoneme*.

Name that team (page 16) provides practice in discriminating between words containing *th* and *ph*. The children could prepare for this as a homework activity. With help they could make up silly jingles containing the phonemes *th* and *f* (spelled *ph*), for example, *Keith brushed his teeth with the telephone*, *Josephine took a photo with her toothbrush*. In class they could share their jingles with their groups and sort the key words into *th* and *ph* lists.

sh or ch (page 17) helps the children to discriminate between the *sh* and *ch* phonemes. It is useful to begin with names the children know and, if necessary, to say the names on this page, leaving the children to identify the correct phoneme to fill the gaps. They could write these and other names containing *sh* or *ch* on slips of paper and sort them into *sh* and *ch* sets. You could also show the children place names in connection with geography lessons: *Ashford, Chester, Colchester, Manchester, Sheffield, Shoreditch, South Shields, Washington.*

Witch words (page 18) practises the *tch* spelling of the *ch* phoneme. The children could use plastic or wooden letters on large phoneme grids to spell words such as *butcher, catch, crutch, ditch, Dutch, fetch, hatch, itch, kitchen, match, pitch, stitch, watch.* Point out that here three letters (a trigraph) stand for the *ch* phoneme.

 **When ch says k** (page 19) introduces common words containing the letters *ch* to represent the phoneme *k*. As a further extension activity you could set a *ch* challenge. Give the children an outline of a Christmas tree on which to write any words they come across in which *ch* says *k*: *ache, Christian, chord, chrome.*

Whee! (page 20) helps the children to recognise the *wh* spelling of the *w* phoneme. Encourage the children to pronounce this slightly differently from *w*: in some regions, *wh* is breathed rather than voiced. This will help them to spell *w* and *wh* words, particularly virtual homophones such as *where/wear, which/witch* and *whether/weather.* Other useful words include: *wheat, wheeze, whisper.*

Tough stuff (page 21) is about recognising the *gh* spelling of the *f* phoneme. Draw out that this does not occur at the beginnings of words and encourage the children to collect other examples of *gh* words. Ask them which vowels *gh* usually follows (*ou* and *au*).

The Knave of Hearts (page 22) focuses on the *kn* spelling of the *n* phoneme in which the *k* is silent. It could be introduced by reciting the nursery rhyme *The Queen of Hearts.*

I'm a gnu (page 23) introduces the *gn* spelling of the *n* phoneme in which the *g* is silent. You can find the words of Flanders and Swann's *Gnu Song* at http://www.poppyfields.net/poppy/songs/gnu.html. You could extend the activity by writing up the word *sign.* Point out that here too the *g* is silent. Some children may be able to think of similar words (*design, foreign, reign*).

Parrot fashion (page 24) is about the double consonant *rr.* It is found more often in the medial position than at the end of a word and, in English, never at the beginning of a word. Other useful words include: *berry, carry, correct, hurry, merry, mirror, porridge, quarrel, sorry.* As a further extension the children could look for words with other

double consonants, such as *bb, dd, ff, gg, ll, mm, nn, pp, ss, tt.* This could be linked with past tenses in which the final consonant doubles: *robbed, begged, fitted.*

Wrong answer (page 25) helps the children to read and spell words that begin with the letters *wr.* They learn that these two letters represent the single phoneme *r.* You could model how to decide on a spelling: begin by saying '*Not right* means *wrong. Wrong* begins with the sound *r.*' Write up *rong*, and then say 'That doesn't look right. It must be a *wr* word.' You could repeat this for other *wr* words such as *wrap, wreath, writing.*

Consonant clusters

These activities feature words containing clusters of two consonants in different positions in the word. The consonants in the clusters are separate phonemes that are blended in speech.

The huffalump (page 26) focuses on words ending in *mp.* Invite the children to contribute to rhymes:

> The huffalump tried to jump
> He jumped, jumped, jumped into the _____ (dump)
> He fell to the ground with a _____ (bump)
> Now his head has a great big _____ (lump).

Ask them to make up similar names ending in *mp*, with a different vowel, for imaginary creatures: *huffalamp, huffalimp.* They could make up rhymes in their groups and use phoneme grids to help them to spell them. Other useful words include: *cramp, dimple, emperor, hump, important, mumps, plump, simple.*

Daft rafts (page 27) helps the children to learn to read and spell words containing the consonant cluster *ft.* Ask them to make up 'daft' sentences using *ft* words: *Fifteen gifts drifted on a raft, Shift the craft into the loft.* Other useful words include: *afternoon, draft, fifty, theft.*

Swim, swan, swim (page 28) helps the children to learn to read and spell words containing the consonant cluster *sw.* You could introduce this with a tongue-twister:

> Swim, swan, swim
> Swim swiftly and straight.

Ask the children to repeat it. Which consonant phoneme do most of the words begin with? Say the tongue-twister more slowly and ask them to listen to the phonemes that follow *s* (*t* and *w*). Ask them to say the words that begin with *sw.* Words they could make by linking three swans include: *swam, swap, swat, sway, sweep, sweet, swell, swill, swim.*

Which tw word? (page 29) helps the children to learn to read and spell words containing the consonant cluster *tw.* You could introduce this with a tongue-twister:

> Tina twisted twine at twilight,
> Tina tried to twirl it and twirl it,
> She tried and tried to twist the twine.

Say the tongue-twister more slowly and ask the children to listen to the phonemes that follow *t* (mainly *r* and *w*). Ask them to say the words that begin with *tw*. Other useful words include: *tweezers, twinkle, twizzle*. The children will have come across the word *two*. Point out that this word is unusual because the *w* is silent.

Vowel phonemes

These activities build on the children's previous learning about the short vowel phonemes *a, e, i, o, u* and the long vowel sounds *ae, ee, ie, oe, ue* produced by adding *e* to form a split digraph, as in *gate* and *bite*. They also introduce the vowel phonemes *oo, ar, ur, au, er, ow, oi, air, ear* and *ure* and show the children that some sounds they have already met may be spelled in a number of ways (*moon, blue, grew*). In some cases they discover that the same spelling may represent more than one phoneme (*bead, bread; zoom, book, flood*).

Snail or whale (page 30) develops the children's repertoire of spelling strategies for the *ae* vowel phoneme. It encourages them to use their knowledge of words formed using *a-e* and to learn new words containing *ai*. Avoid words containing *are* and *air* because these introduce a new vowel phoneme (see pages 47 and 48). Some useful dictation sentences include: *Chase the waiter with the plate, Make a plate of raisin cake, Paint a face on the daisy, It's too late to chain the gate.*

Glue clues (page 31) is about the *ue* vowel phoneme. Note that in some words (and only in some regions) *ue* sounds more like *yu*: *due, duel, fuel, hue.*

Jewels (page 32) focuses on the *ew* spelling of the vowel phoneme *ue*. It begins with simple three- and four-letter words. Others include: *flew, newt, screw, stew.* Point out that *ew* combines two letters to make one vowel sound.

A good book (page 33) develops the children's knowledge of words containing the *oo* spelling pattern. Remind them of their previous learning about *oo* saying the *ue* phoneme (as in *zoom* and *moon*). Note that *oo* can also stand for the *oo* phoneme (as in *good* and *book*) and for the short *u* sound (as in *blood*, to rhyme with *mud*). Depending on regional pronunciation, you could also introduce words such as *cook, crook, hood, look, took.*

Car park (page 34) develops the children's knowledge of vowel digraphs – *ar* is a single phoneme represented by two letters. Other useful words include: *arm, art, barn, carpet, charge, farm, large, marble, march, market, Mars, parcel, part, sardine, smart, start.*

Beads (page 35) develops spelling strategies for the *ee* vowel phoneme. It encourages the children to use their knowledge of words formed using *ee* and to learn new words containing *ea*. They could make a beads wall display showing *ea* words that say *ee*.

As heavy as lead (page 36) focuses on the *ea* spelling of the *e* vowel phoneme. Avoid words containing *ear* such as *earth, heart, hearth* because these introduce new vowel phonemes. To complement work on page 35 you could make a display of *ea* words that say *e*. Divide the board in two and ask the children to place heavy things with *ea* in their name on one side and label them and place light things with *ea* in their name on the other side and label them:

heavy as lead	light as a feather
leather shoe	yellow thread

Coins (page 37) is about the *oi* vowel phoneme. Encourage the children to make up rhymes using *oi* words:

Oi, oi, oi,
Boil the oil!
Oi, oi, oi,
Pour it on the soil.

Oi, oi, oi,
Let's hear your voice!
Oi, oi ,oi,
You have no choice.

Other useful words include: *noise, point, poison*. Point out that in English we do not find *oi* at the end of a word. Note that the two letters make one vowel sound.

Ship ahoy! (page 38) features the spelling pattern *oy* representing the vowel phoneme *oi*. The children will probably know several of these  words already, for example, *boy, toy*. They could also create *oy* words by adding letters to the beginning and/or end of *oy*: *annoy, cowboy, enjoy, soya*. Emphasise that *oy* combines two letters to make one vowel sound.

Brown cow (page 39) is about the vowel phoneme *ow*. Draw out that *ow* combines two letters to make one vowel sound. The children can make the following words: *cow, cowl, down, fowl, gown, how, howl, now, sow, vow*. Other useful words include: *allow, clown, crowd, crown, drown, flower, growl, shower, tower, towel, town, vowel, wow.*

Ouch! (page 40) is about the *ou* spelling of the *ow* vowel phoneme. Draw out that *ou* combines two vowels to make one vowel sound. The children can make words from the following list: *cloud, count, found, noun, pound, proud, round, scout, shout, sound, spout, sprout*. Other useful words include: *aloud, amount, around, blouse, bounce, couch, crouch, fountain, ground, mountain, mouse, our, out, south, thousand, trousers*. If the children generate words such as *pour* and *four*, read the words with them and point out the different phoneme produced by the grapheme *ou*.

Yoyos (page 41) features the *oe* vowel phoneme (spelled *o* or *oe*) at the end of a word. The children can make the following words: *go, so, no, ago, yoyo, dodo, hippo, tomato; hoe, Joe, foe, woe*. Other useful words include: *disco, domino, goes, hello, photo, piano, potato, radio, video, zero.*

Glow-worms (page 42) helps the children to learn that the same letters can represent different phonemes. This activity features the *ow* spelling of the *oe* phoneme. The children could make a 'glow-worms' display by cutting out glow-worm outlines from fluorescent paper and writing *ow* words on them. Other useful words include: *borrow, know, mow, narrow, rainbow, row, shadow, throw, window*.

Pies in the sky and **High and dry** (pages 43–44) help the children to learn that some phonemes can be represented by different letters. These activities feature the *ie*, *y* and *igh* spellings of the *ie* phoneme. Begin by reading the poem 'Sky in the Pie!' by Roger McGough (from *Sky in the Pie*, Puffin). Point out the two spellings of the *ie* phoneme and ask the children if they can find any other words in the poem that contain this sound (*quite, light, night*).

Mrs Lear's ears (page 45) features the vowel phoneme *ear* (as in *ears*). The children could also build words by adding letters to precede or follow *ear* (and which sound the same): *beard, dreary, nearly, shears, spear, year*.

Pieces of eight (page 46) helps the children to understand that some phonemes can be represented in writing by different letters. This features the *eigh* and *ei* spellings of the *ae* phoneme. Other useful words include: *eighteen, eighteenth, eighth, eighty, freight, reign, sleigh*.

 Airy fairy, **A fair share**, **Word turns**, **Chirping birds** and **Pears or pearls?** (pages 47–51) feature different spellings of the *air* and *ur* phonemes. They help the children to learn that a phoneme can be represented in writing by different letters. On page 49, the children can make the following words: *fern, herb, herd, kerb, word, work, worm, burn, churn, curd, curl, furl, hurl, lurk*. If they make words such as *cork, form* or *worn*, ask them to say the word. Point out that this is a different vowel phoneme (the *au* phoneme – see page 52). Give the children a copy of this verse and ask them to underline the different spellings of the *air* phoneme in different colours:

'A bear was there – on the stair –
A bear with fair hair,' said Clare.
'We do not care about the bear –
on the stair or anywhere,'
Said her parents to Clare
As they sat in the chair.

Corks and forks (page 52) focuses on the common spelling pattern *or* for the vowel phoneme *au*. Other useful words include: *acorn, cornflakes, dormouse, for, more, normal, store, story, tore, torpedo, worn*.

A pure cure (page 53) helps the children to identify and spell the vowel phoneme *ure* in words such as *cure, pure* and *plural*. Point out how this is different from the sound and spelling patterns of the *ur* phoneme in *burst, curse, hurt* and *purse*. Explain that the phoneme that follows *ur* in these words is always a consonant. Compare this with the *ure* phoneme in *cure, manure, mature, mural* and *Uranus*. In these words the *ur* grapheme is followed by a

vowel. The children who work on the extension activity should notice that in *fury* and *jury* the *y* acts as a vowel.

Consolidation

These activities encourage the children to use their knowledge of phonics to recognise the different ways in which sounds are written in order to read them correctly and to choose the correct letters to represent a phoneme in order to help them to spell words accurately. The activities pull together previous learning and can be used to assess understanding and progress.

Choose and chews (page 54) focuses on four spellings of the *ue* vowel phoneme and reinforces learning that the same phoneme may be spelled in different ways.

Thanks for this (page 55) focuses on the slightly different phonemes represented by *th* and reinforces previous learning of the initial consonant digraph *th*.

Hard or soft c and **Hard or soft g** (pages 56–57) reinforce previous learning of words with hard and soft *c* and *g* phonemes. Encourage the children to use the words in each creature to make alliterative jingles, rhymes and so on.

Say the k (page 58) reinforces and extends the children's learning about the *k* consonant phoneme and the *n* consonant phoneme spelled *kn* where the *k* is silent.

Hear the g (page 59) reinforces and extends the children's learning about the *g* consonant phoneme and the *n* consonant phoneme spelled *gn* where the *g* is silent.

Beans on bread (page 60) consolidates and extends the children's learning about the different vowel phonemes represented in writing by *ea*: the short *e* sound in *bread* and the long *ee* sound in *beans*.

Hares and chairs (page 61) reinforces and extends the children's learning about the *air* and *are* spellings of the *air* vowel phoneme.

Short straws (page 62) reinforces and extends the children's learning about the *or* spelling of the vowel phoneme *au* and introduces the *aw* digraph for the same sound. Other useful *aw* words include: *brawl, dawn, flaw, law, pawn, raw, saw, scrawl, thaw, yawn*.

Fill the gap: er, ir, ur (page 63) consolidates the ability to use phonics to spell words containing the *ur* vowel phoneme. Invite the children to consider alternative spellings, for example, *iceberg* or *iceburg*. Ask them to decide which is more likely to be right. They could put 1 or 2 next to each one before looking them up.

Phantom phonemes (page 64) is a challenging activity for which many children will need support. They could work in pairs. One could select a vowel digraph or trigraph from the phantom's list and the other could look for a word below to fit the phoneme.

Soft [c]

A soft [c] sounds like [s].

- **Read the soft [c] words.**
- **Read the clues.**
- **Write the soft [c] words.**

Word bank

city

face

icy

lace

mice

pencil

race

Your eyes, nose and mouth are on it.

_____

You use this to tie your shoe.

_____

Very cold.

_____

A big town.

_____

Run very fast.

_____

More than one mouse.

_____

You write with it.

_____

Which letters follow the soft [c]?

[ ] [ ] [ ]

NOW try this!

Teachers' note With the children, read the words in the word bank. Draw attention to the *s* phoneme represented by *c*. Ask what each word means. Model how to complete the first example. Link this to the children's previous learning about long vowel phonemes.

Developing Literacy
Phonics
Book 3
© A & C BLACK

Soft g

A soft g sounds like j.

- **Read the soft g words.**
- **Read the clues.**
- **Write the soft g words.**

Word bank
cage
Gemma
germ
giant
giraffe
page
Roger

You can keep a mouse in this.

_____

A very, very tall animal.

_____

This can make you ill.

_____

A girl's name.

_____

A boy's name.

_____

Part of a book.

_____

A very, very tall person.

_____

Which letters follow the soft g ?

☐ ☐

Teachers' note With the children, read the words in the word bank. Draw attention to the _j_ phoneme represented by _g_. Ask what each word means. Model how to complete the first example. Link this to the children's previous learning about long vowel phonemes.

Developing Literacy
Phonics
Book 3
© A & C BLACK

Easy does it

- **Look at the pictures.**
- **Fill in the letters.**
- **Read the words.**

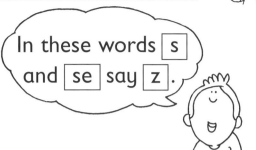
In these words s *and* se *say* z *.*

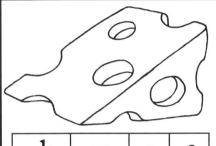
| ch | ee | s | e |

| d | ai | | y |

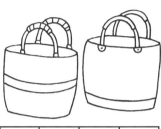
| b | | | |

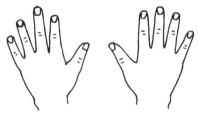
| h | | | |

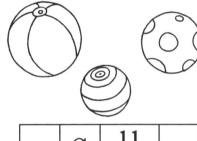
| | a | ll | |

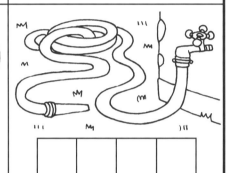
| | | | |

| | | | |

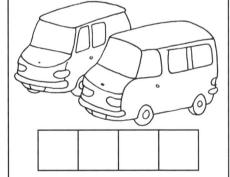
| | | | |

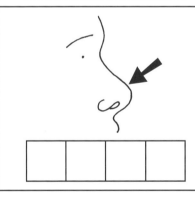
| | | | |

- **Write the missing letters.**
- **Read the words.**

| h | i | |

| ch | oo | |

In these words s *and* se *say* z *.*

| pl | ea | |

| bl | ou | |

Teachers' note Write up the word *as* and ask the children what it says. What sound does the *s* stand for? Draw out that *s* can stand for the *z* sound as well as the *s* they know. Ensure that they recognise the word suggested by each picture. Emphasise the *z* sound of the *s*. Point out that the children should write one letter in each box.

Developing Literacy
Phonics
Book 3
© A & C BLACK

11

Lazy daisy

- **Say the words.**

- **Listen to the** ⬚ s .

- **If the** ⬚ s **says** ⬚ z **, write the word on the daisy.**

Word bank

as	ask	bus	dogs	easy	has
mask	please	snap	these	those	wise

Daisy

- **Write the words.**

Now try this!

 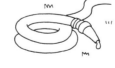

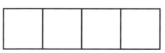

| ch | ee | | | | | | | | | | | |

Teachers' note Ask volunteers to read aloud the words in the word bank. After each one, ask the class if the *s* said *s* or *z*. Emphasise that the only words they should write on the daisy are those in which *s* says *z*. Show the children how to turn the page so that they can write horizontally on the petals.

**Developing Literacy
Phonics
Book 3
© A & C BLACK**

This and that

- **Cut out the shapes.**
- **Make words that begin with**  **th** **, like**  **th i s and th a t .**
- **Say the words.**
- **Listen to** **th** **.**

The shapes must fit together.

a   s   e   t   o

th   i   se   ey   n

Now try this!

- **Finish the sentence with a** **th** **word.**

My house is over _____.

Teachers' note Demonstrate the pronunciation of *th* in *this* and *that* (see **Notes on the activities**, page 5). Ask the children to cut out the shapes. Model how to fit them together to make words. The children should not glue down the words they make so that they can re-use the phonemes. If they make the word *thin* point out that it is not a correct *th* word here and explain why.

Developing Literacy
Phonics
Book 3
© A & C BLACK

Thick and thin

- **Cut out the shapes.**
- **Make words that begin with  th, like**

 th i ck **and** th i n .

- **Say the words.**
- **Listen to** th .

The shapes must fit together.

a   n   d   th   or

i   ck   k   n   u

- **Write** th **words for:**

3   13   30

_____   _____   _____

Teachers' note Demonstrate the pronunciation of *th* in *thick* and *thin* (see **Notes on the activities**, page 5). Ask the children to cut out the shapes. Model how to fit them together to make words. The children should not glue down the words they make so that they can re-use the phonemes. If the children make the word *than* point out that it is not a correct *th* word here and explain why.

Developing Literacy
Phonics
Book 3
© A & C BLACK

ph says f

- **Complete the** ph **words.**
- **Read the words.**

Write the letters for one phoneme in each box.

Think of a boy's name.

| | i | l | i | p |

| | o | t | o | |

| | | n | e |

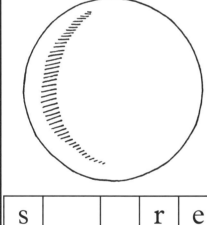

| s | | | r | e |

| t | r | o | | |

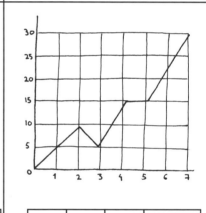

| g | r | | |

- **Write the word.**

Now try this!

a b c d e f g h i j k l m n o p q r s t u v w x y z

| a | l | | a | | |

- **Write a girl's name.**

| S | | | ie |

Teachers' note You could begin by saying three words containing the *ph* spelling of the *f* phoneme: for example, *elephant*, *aphid*, *phoneme*. Ask the children which sound is in all the words. How would they write this phoneme? If they say *f*, introduce *ph* as one alternative spelling. Point out that the two letters *ph* stand for one phoneme.

Developing Literacy
Phonics
Book 3
© A & C BLACK

Name that team

- **Read the children's names.**
- **Listen for the** `th` **or** `f` **sound.**
- **Write the names on the football team lists.**

Football teams

`th`	`f`

Raphael
Bethan
Josephine

Faith
Phillipa
Joseph
Delphine

Kenneth
Aphra
Ralph
Dorothy

Edith
Keith
Gareth
Rudolph

Cathy
Phyllis
Thelma
Judith

Zeph
Stephan
Tabitha

- **Write four words with** `th` **and four words with** `f` **spelled** `ph` **.**

Now try this!

Teachers' note Some children might need help with this activity. Demonstrate the phonemes represented by *th* and *ph*. Read the names and ask the children which phoneme they hear. Point out that this activity uses the breathed *th*, as in *thick*. Ask them to underline the *f* and *th* phonemes in the names using a different colour for each. They can then copy them onto the team lists.

Developing Literacy
Phonics
Book 3
© A & C BLACK

sh or ch

- **Complete the children's names with**

sh or **ch** .

- **Read the names.**

Ri ☐ ard

☐ ona

Raje ☐

☐ arlie

☐ elley

Jo ☐

Ay ☐ a

Kri ☐ na

Ra ☐ el

☐ aron

Nata ☐ a

Hami ☐

- **Look around the classroom for**

sh and **ch** **words.**

- **List them.**

Teachers' note Remind the children of their previous learning about the phonemes represented by *sh* and *ch*. Read the names aloud and ask the children to repeat them. Draw attention to the *sh* or *ch* phoneme in each name.

Developing Literacy
Phonics
Book 3
© A & C BLACK

17

Witch words

- **Make** tch **words.**
- **Link the stars to endings on the cauldron.**
- **Write the words.**
- **Read the words.**

Witch words

h   c   d

l   f

m

n

a | tch   e | tch

i | tch   o | tch

p

w

- **Write the** tch **words.**

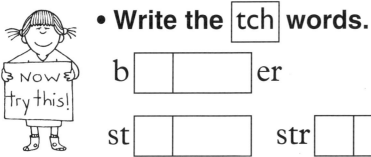

b [　|　] er

st [　|　]   str [　|　]

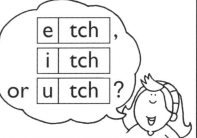

e | tch ,
i | tch
or u | tch ?

Teachers' note Remind the children of their previous learning about the *ch* phoneme. Tell them that the same phoneme can be written *tch*. You could use words such as *itch* and *kitchen* as examples.

Developing Literacy
Phonics
Book 3
© A & C BLACK

When ☐ch☐ says ☐k☐

In some words and names ☐ch☐ says ☐k☐.

- Write ☐ch☐ in each word.

- Read the words.

☐ ristmas

☐ ristopher

☐ löe

☐ ristine

☐ oir

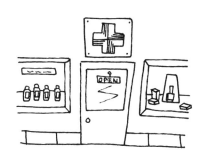
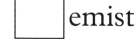

☐ emist

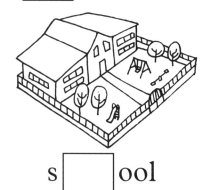

s ☐ ool

- **Write three other words where ☐ch☐ says ☐k☐.**

  Clues: A person in a story.

  A repeated part of a song.

  A sound which bounces back so we hear it again.

Teachers' note Write up *ch* and remind the children of their previous learning about *ch* words. Can they think of any names that begin with *ch*? Begin with names of children in the class, in their families or in other classes in the school. Ask them what sound the *ch* makes. Point out that *ch* sometimes says *k*.

Developing Literacy
Phonics
Book 3
© A & C BLACK

19

The words on the fireworks begin with wh **.**

- **Write** wh **.**

- **Read the words.**

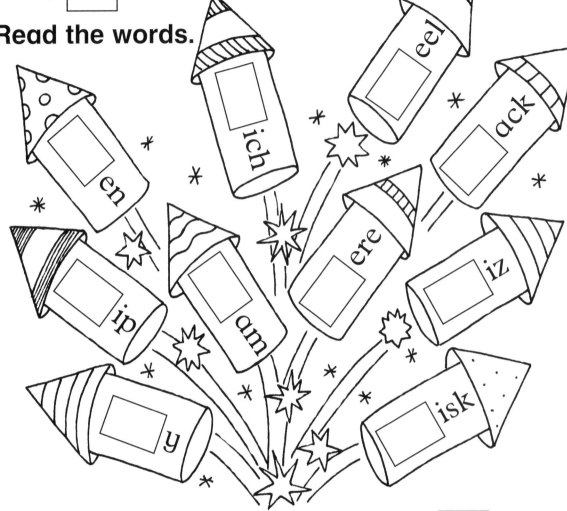

- **Make up a sentence using as many** wh **words as you can.**

_____

_____

- **Complete the sentences with a** wh **word.**

Snow is _____.

You can blow a _____.

Teachers' note Write up *w* and ask the children which phoneme it stands for (*w*). Tell them that the same phoneme can also be written *wh*. Explain that according to the region *wh* may be pronounced in exactly the same way as *w* or it may sound more like *hw* as it is given more of a breathed pronunciation. Show the children how to turn the page to write horizontally on the rockets.

Developing Literacy
Phonics
Book 3
© A & C BLACK

Tough stuff

- **Say the rhyming words.**
- **Draw a box around** gh .

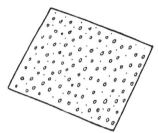

rough stuff

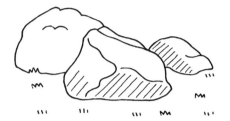

tough stuff

enough stuff

Cough your head off.

half a laugh

Scoff at the trough.

- **Cover the top part of the page.**
- **Write the rhyming words on the grids.**

off | c | | |

stuff | t | | |

half | l | | |

scoff | t | r | | |

Write the letters for one phoneme in each box.

Teachers' note Remind the children of their previous work on the *f* phoneme: for example, the single *f* at the beginnings of words such as *fit*, *full* and *five* and the double *ff* at the ends of words such as *cuff*, *puff* and *stuff*. Also remind them of *ph* in *phone* and *photo*. Tell them that *gh* at the end or in the middle of a word can also say *f*. You could use *laugh* as an example.

Developing Literacy
Phonics
Book 3
© A & C BLACK

The Knave of Hearts

The Knave of Hearts has a silent $\boxed{k}$ **.**

- **Write** $\boxed{kn}$ **at the beginning of each word.**

- **Read the words.**

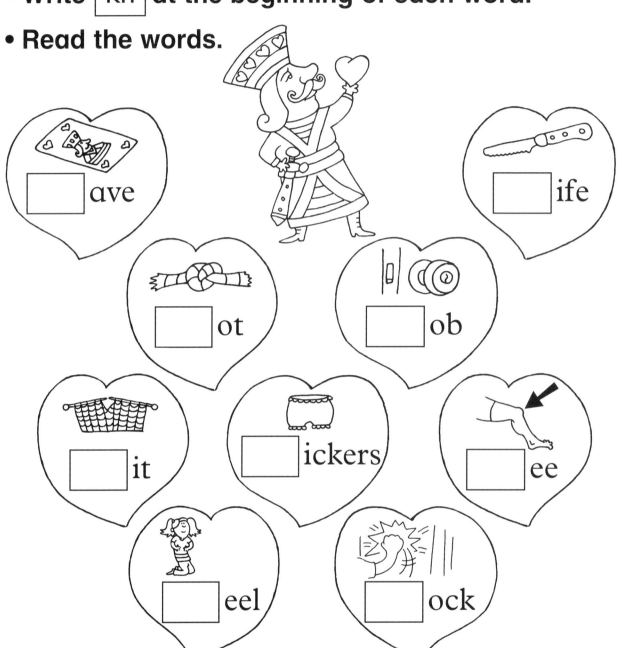

$\boxed{}$ave

$\boxed{}$ife

$\boxed{}$ot

$\boxed{}$ob

$\boxed{}$it

$\boxed{}$ickers

$\boxed{}$ee

$\boxed{}$eel

$\boxed{}$ock

Now try this!

- **Write three other** $\boxed{kn}$ **words.**

  Clues: A soldier who wore armour.

  Part of your hand.

  In a test you show what you _____.

Teachers' note Begin with the nursery rhyme *The Queen of Hearts* and explain *knave*. You could show the Knave (Jack) of Hearts from a pack of cards. Invite the children to try to spell *knave*. Attempts such as *nave* or even *nayv* should be given credit for choosing letters that stand for the *n* and long *a* phonemes. Tell them that *knave* is one of a few words in which the *n* sound is spelled *kn*.

Developing Literacy
Phonics
Book 3
© **A & C BLACK**

I'm a gnu

Gnu has a silent `g`**.**

The *Gnu Song* lets you hear it.

I'm a gnu — the g-nicest work of g-nature in the zoo.

I'm a gnu, a-g-nother gnu — I wish I could g-nash my teeth at you.

- **Write** `gn` **in the gaps.**
- **Read the sentences.**

I'm a ☐ ome. I'm not a ☐ u.

I'm a ☐ at. I have no teeth to ☐ ash.

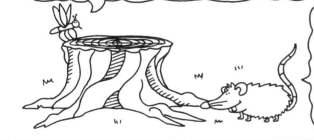

I'm a rat. I ☐ aw the ☐ arled tree.

- **Make up a song for the gnome.**
- **Sing it with a friend.**

Teachers' note Begin with Flanders and Swann's *Gnu Song* (see **Notes on the activities**, page 6) in which as a joke the silent *g* of *gnu* is pronounced throughout. Read or sing the verses of the song with the children. Help them to find the words to which for fun *g* has been added incorrectly. Can they find a *n* word in which the *g* has been added correctly? (*gnash*)

Developing Literacy
Phonics
Book 3
© A & C BLACK

Parrot fashion

- **Read the parrot's clues.**
- **Write the** | rr | **words.**
- **Read the words.**

Lovely bird.

| | | rr | | |

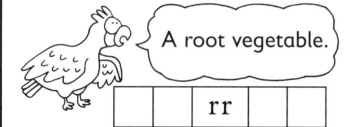

A root vegetable.

| | | rr | | |

Word bank

barrel
carrot
curry
narrow
parrot
sorrow

Thin.

| | rr | |

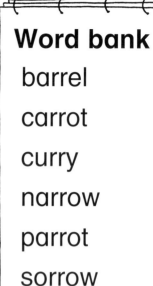

A big
wooden tub.

| | | rr | | |

Sadness.

| | rr | |

A spicy meal.

| | | rr | |

- **Write the** | rr | **words.**
- **Read the words.**

Now try this!

| s | p | rr | |

| b | | | ow |

| b | | | ow |

| t | o | m | | | |

Teachers' note Write up the letter *r* and ask the children what phoneme it stands for. Say the word *parrot* and ask the children if they hear the phoneme *r*. Was it at the beginning, in the middle or at the end of the word? Help the children to write it on a phoneme grid. Point out the double *r*. Tell them that they are going to learn other words with double *r*. Do any of them have a name with double *r*?

Developing Literacy
Phonics
Book 3
© A & C BLACK

Wrong answer

- **Read the clue.**

- **Say the answer.**

- **Write the answer.**

The answers begin with wr .

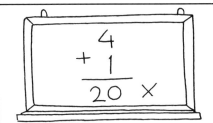

Not right.

| | o | |

You | | a | p | a present.

Where your hand joins your arm.

| | i | s | t |

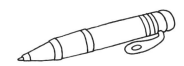

You | | i | t | e | with a pen.

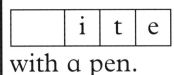

You | | i | | a wet cloth.

A ship that sank.

| | e | ck |

A worm can do this.

| | | gg | l | e |

A very small bird.

| | | n |

A line on a face.

| | | n | k | l | e |

- **Make a** wr **word from the letters in the box.**

| t | | o | | e |
| | wr | |

_____

Teachers' note Write up the letters *wr* and say the phoneme they stand for. Point out that the two letters *w* and *r* together stand for the single *r* phoneme. Model aloud the thought process for the first clue (see **Notes on the activities**, page 6) before asking the children to complete the sheet independently.

Developing Literacy
Phonics
Book 3
© A & C BLACK

The huffalump

The huffalump collects words with [m][p].

- **Complete the** [m][p] **words.**

- **Read the words.**

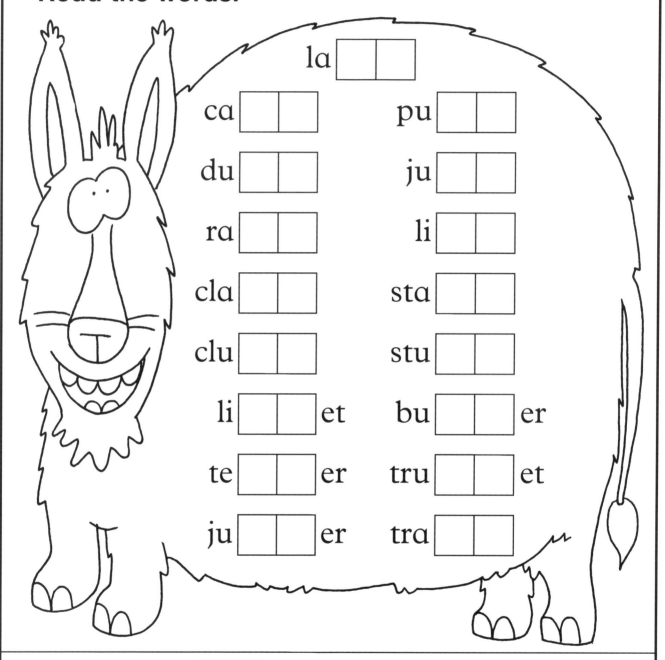

la[ ][ ]

ca[ ][ ]   pu[ ][ ]

du[ ][ ]   ju[ ][ ]

ra[ ][ ]   li[ ][ ]

cla[ ][ ]   sta[ ][ ]

clu[ ][ ]   stu[ ][ ]

li[ ][ ]et   bu[ ][ ]er

te[ ][ ]er   tru[ ][ ]et

ju[ ][ ]er   tra[ ][ ]

- **Write** [m][p] **words for:**

  – a truck for moving earth and rocks

  – a bit wet.

Teachers' note Say the words *bump, lamp, damp, chimp* and *clamp*. Which two phonemes do they end with? Ask the children which letters stand for these phonemes. Can they think of any other words with *mp* in them? Point out the title of this page and invite the children to try reading it. After they have completed the words invite volunteers to read different words aloud.

Developing Literacy
Phonics
Book 3
© A & C BLACK

Daft rafts

- **Fill in the gaps to make** $\boxed{\text{f}\ \text{t}}$ **words.**
- **Read the words.**

Teachers' note Write up the letter *f* and ask the children to say the phoneme it stands for. Follow it with a letter *t* and ask them to say the phoneme it stands for. Now can they put the two phonemes together and say them one after the other (*ft*)? Add a vowel in front of them, for example, *ift*, *oft*. Ask the children to complete the *ft* words on the rafts. Some might need the vowel phonemes to be filled in first.

Developing Literacy
Phonics
Book 3
© A & C BLACK

27

Swim, swan, swim

- **Link three swans to make** [s][w] **words.**
- **Write the words.**
- **Read the words.**

Use one swan from each river.

sw

a   e   ee   i

ll   m   p   t   y

[s][w] **words**

swam

• **Write the** [s][w] **words.**

NOW try this!

Teachers' note Begin with a jingle such as *Swim, swan, swim; Swish and swash and swim; Swim, swan, swim.* Ask the children which phoneme they heard at the beginning of most words. Which phoneme came next? Write up the letters *s* and *w* as they identify the phonemes. Show them how to link three swans on this page to make a word. They should write the letters in a swan outline on the notepad to make words.

Developing Literacy
Phonics
Book 3
© A & C BLACK

28

Which [t][w] word?

- **Choose a [t][w] word.**

  Can your partner guess which one?

| t | w | i | n | s |

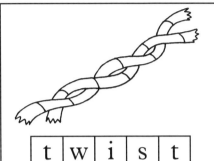

| t | w | i | s | t |

| t | w | e | l | v | e |

| t | w | e | n | t | y |

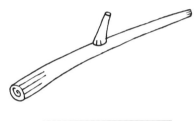

| t | w | i | g |

| t | w | ee | t |

| t | w | ir | l |

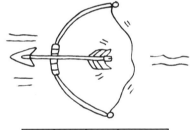

| t | w | a | ng |

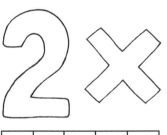

| t | w | i | c | e |

| t | w | i | tt | er |

| t | w | i | n | e |

| t | w | i | tch |

NOW try this!

- **Cover this page.**
- **Write four [t][w] words.**

Teachers' note This is a game for two players. Each has a copy of the page and some cubes or counters for covering eliminated words. Player 1 chooses a word. Player 2 has to find out which it is by asking questions with yes/no answers, for example, is the third letter *i*? Does it have five phonemes? He or she covers the words eliminated by each answer. Once the word has been identified it is Player 2's turn.

Developing Literacy
Phonics
Book 3
© A & C BLACK

Snail or whale

- Look at the pictures.
- Say the words.
- Think how to spell them.
- Write them on the snail or the whale.

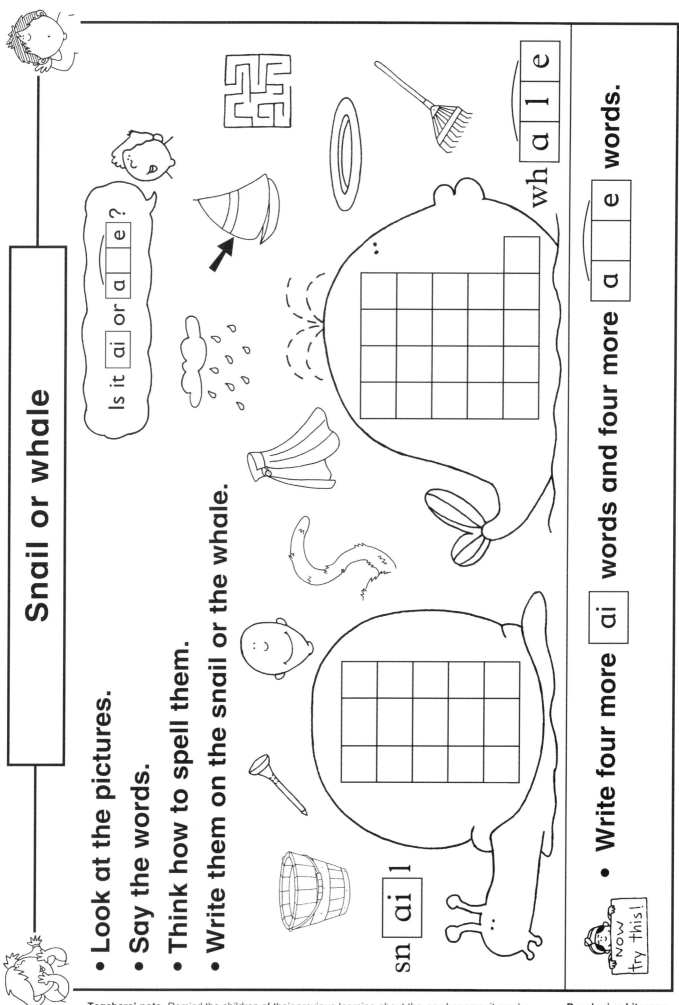

Is it [ai] or [a][ ][e]?

wh [a] [l] [e]

sn [ai] l

- Write four more [ai] words and four more [a][ ][e] words.

Now try this!

Teachers' note Remind the children of their previous learning about the *ae* phoneme: it can be written *a-e* as in *late*, *cape*, *bake* or *ai* as in *mail*, *pain*, *main*, *raid*. Ask them to say the words for the pictures and to decide which is correct – *a-e* or *ai*. They could look up the words if necessary.

Developing Literacy Phonics Book 3 © A & C BLACK

Glue clues

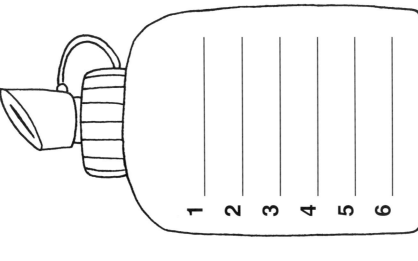

- **ue** can make the long **u** sound.
- **Complete the ue words and read them aloud.**
- **Read the clue for each number.**
- **Write the words on the bottle of glue.**

b	l	

c	l	

g	l	

c	r	l

S		r

t	r	

1 Girl's name. Short for Susan.
2 The colour of the sky.
3 A _____ helps you to work out a puzzle.
4 A fact is something _____ .
5 When someone is unkind or nasty.
6 Sticky stuff.

- **Cover this page except for the clues.**
- **Write the words.**

NOW
try this!

Teachers' note Remind the children of their previous learning about the *oo* spelling of the *ue* phoneme (*zoom*, *moon*). Write up *ue* and tell them that this makes the same long *u* sound. Ask them to fill in the gaps in the words with *ue*. Ask volunteers to read the words aloud. Read the clues with them and then ask them to match a word to each clue.

Jewels

ew can make the long u sound.

- Write ew words on the jewels.
- Read the words.

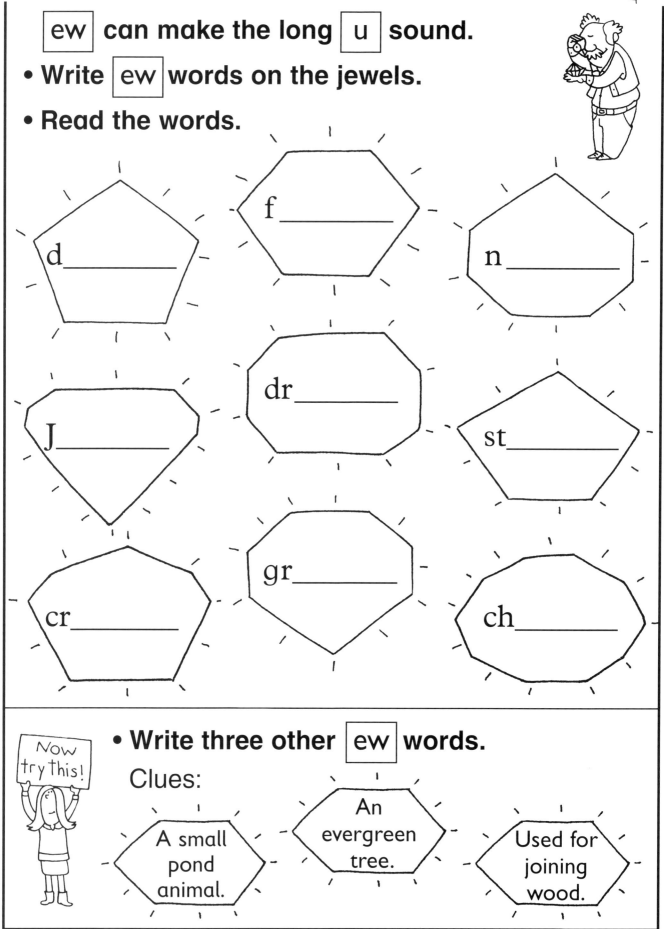

d_____

f_____

n_____

J_____

dr_____

st_____

cr_____

gr_____

ch_____

- Write three other ew words.

Clues:

A small pond animal.

An evergreen tree.

Used for joining wood.

Teachers' note Write up *ew* and demonstrate how to pronounce the phoneme. (It says the name of the letter *u*.) You could use it in sentences such as *I have a few new jewels*, *The newt grew and grew*, *Chew the stew*. You could introduce new vocabulary such as the name of the tree *yew* (draw out the different spelling from *you* – also the female sheep *ewe*) and *screw*, used in woodwork.

**Developing Literacy
Phonics
Book 3
© A & C BLACK**

A good book

- **Join the phonemes to make** oo **words.**
- **Read the words.**
- **Find two words where** oo **says** u **.**
- **Circle them in red.**

g oo d _____

b oo k _____

w oo l _____

w oo d _____

b l oo d _____

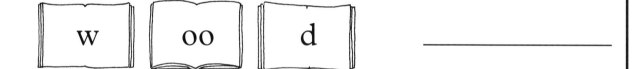
f l oo d _____

- **Write three** oo **words that rhyme with** book **.**

Teachers' note Tell the children that all the words on this page have *oo* in the middle but two are pronounced differently from the rest. Ask them to join the phonemes on each row of books to make an *oo* word and then to read it aloud. Can they hear which two sound different? You could help some children by asking them to listen for the words that rhyme with *mud*. They should circle the two odd words in red.

**Developing Literacy
Phonics
Book 3
© A & C BLACK**

Car park

- **Write the** `ar` **words.**
- **Read the words.**

| c | ar |

| p | | |

| | | |

| | |

| | | |

| | | |

| | | |

| | | |

| | | |

- **Re-write these mixed-up** `ar` **words:**

| ar | m | k |

| d | h | ar |

| p | t | ar |

| l | ar | a | m |

Teachers' note Ask the children if they can spell *far*. You could use a phoneme grid to help them. Some children might spell it *fr*, using the single letter *r* (by its name) to represent the phoneme *ar*. Remind them that *r* stands for the phoneme *r* (use words such as *rat*, *rib* and *rug* to demonstrate). Help them to use phoneme grids to spell *far* and *tar* before they begin the activities on this page.

Developing Literacy
Phonics
Book 3
© A & C BLACK

Beads

In beads | ea | says | ee |.

- Write | ea | words on the beads.

- Read the words.

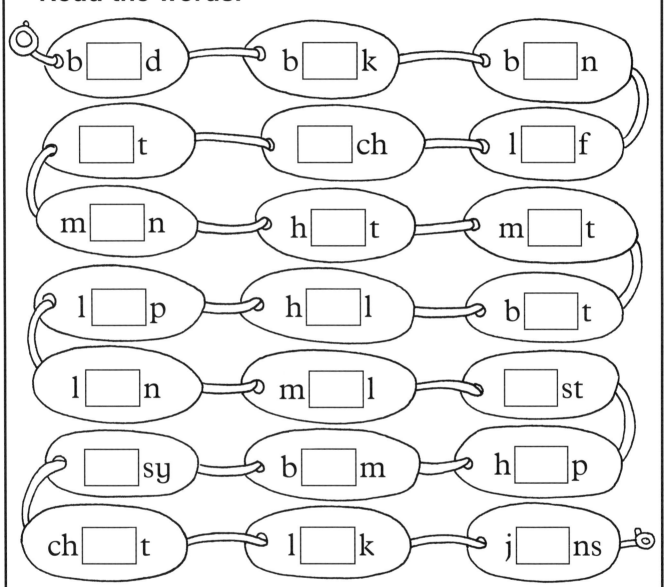

b[ ]d   b[ ]k   b[ ]n

[ ]t   [ ]ch   l[ ]f

m[ ]n   h[ ]t   m[ ]t

l[ ]p   h[ ]l   b[ ]t

l[ ]n   m[ ]l   [ ]st

[ ]sy   b[ ]m   h[ ]p

ch[ ]t   l[ ]k   j[ ]ns

- Write the | ea | words for:

  – a big meal   f[ ][ ][ ]

  – doesn't cost much   ch[ ][ ]

  – a disease   m[ ][ ]les

Now try this!

Teachers' note Begin by saying *Lee sees three beads*. Ask which is the main phoneme. Invite a volunteer to write the letters that stand for the *ee* phoneme. On the board, help the children to write *ee* words such as *see*, *feed*, *feel*, *deep*. Tell them that this phoneme can also be written *ea*. Show them the example – *bead*. After they have completed the *ea* words, invite volunteers to take turns to read them aloud.

**Developing Literacy
Phonics
Book 3
© A & C BLACK**

As heavy as lead

ea can say **e** .

- **Write the missing letters.**

- **Read the words.**

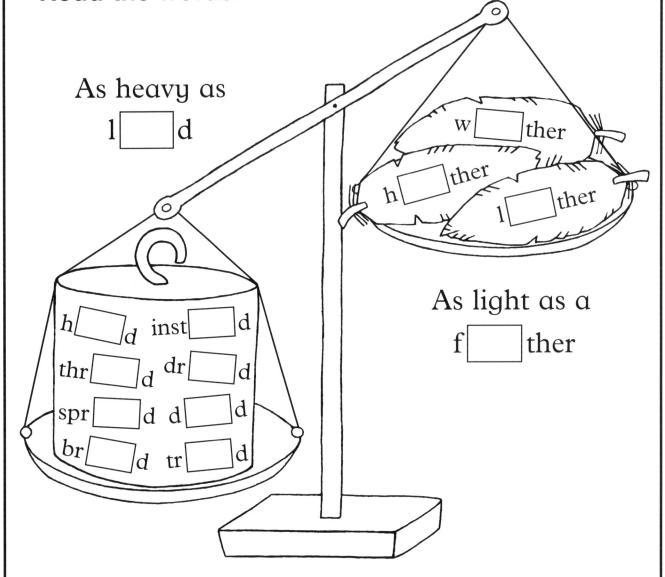

As heavy as
l☐d

w☐ther

h☐ther

l☐ther

As light as a
f☐ther

h☐d inst☐d

thr☐d dr☐d

spr☐d d☐d

br☐d tr☐d

Now try this!

- **Write** **ea** **words in the gaps.**

R☐☐y, st☐☐y – go!

If you are h☐☐y, you are well.

If you are w☐☐y, you are rich.

Teachers' note Remind the children of their previous learning about the *ea* spelling of the *ee* phoneme. Tell them that *ea* can also stand for the *e* sound. Emphasise that the letters *ea* stand for one phoneme. Write up the words *heavy* and *lead* and invite volunteers to read them aloud. During the plenary session ask the children to read the words on this page aloud.

Developing Literacy
Phonics
Book 3
© A & C BLACK

Coins

- **Complete the** oi **words on the coins.**
- **Write them on the piggy bank.**
- **Read the words.**

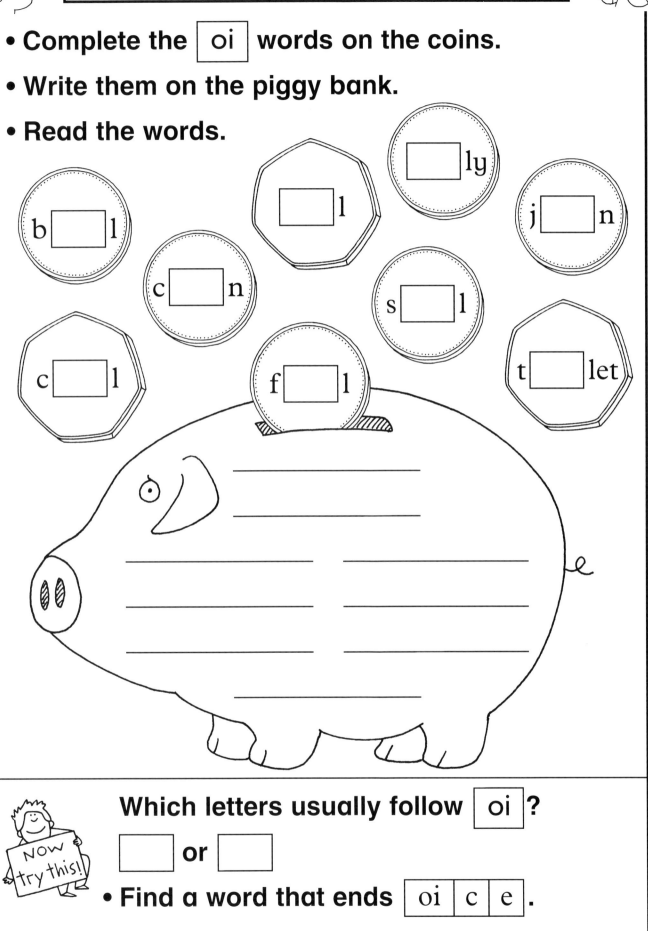

b☐l

☐ly

☐l

j☐n

c☐n

c☐l

s☐l

f☐l

t☐let

Teachers' note Write up *oi*. You could introduce the phoneme in a jingle: *Oi! Oi! Boil the oil! Oi! Oi! Don't spoil the soil*. Invite the children to make up '*Oi*' jingles (the spellings do not matter – it is the *oi* phoneme that is the focus). After they have completed the *oi* words, ask them to take turns to read them aloud. Draw out that no words end in *oi*; *oi* is often followed by *l* or *n*.

Ship ahoy!

- **Join the ships to the buoy to make oy words.**

- **Write the words.**

- **Read the words.**

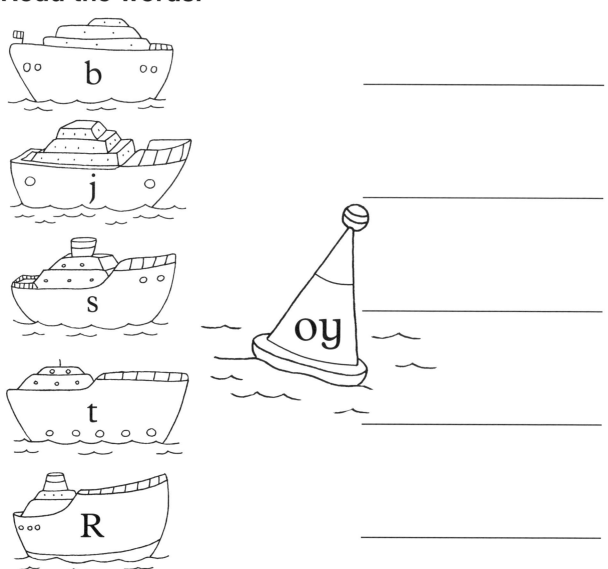

- **Make up a rhyme using your oy words.**

- **Complete these oy words.**

    J☐ce   ☐ster   r☐al

- **Read them.**

Teachers' note Remind the children of the *oi* phoneme. Tell them that it can also be spelled *oy*. Do they know any words or names that end in *oy*? Examples include *boy*, *Roy*, *joy*. Note that the *oi* phoneme is spelled *oy* if it comes at the end of a word. Also point out the unusual spelling of *buoy*.

**Developing Literacy
Phonics
Book 3
© A & C BLACK**

Brown cow

- **Cut out the shapes.**

- **Make** ow **words.**

The shapes must fit together.

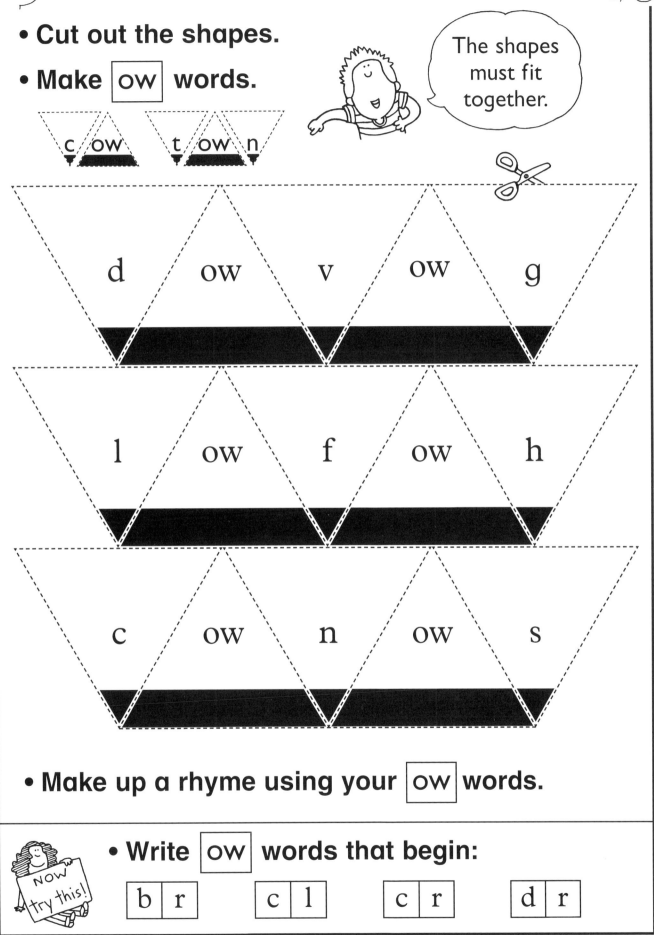

c ow   t ow n

d   ow   v   ow   g

l   ow   f   ow   h

c   ow   n   ow   s

- **Make up a rhyme using your** ow **words.**

- **Write** ow **words that begin:**

| b | r | | c | l | | c | r | | d | r |

NOW try this!

Teachers' note This could be introduced through the question *How now brown cow?* Ask the children if they can spell the *ow* phoneme. They could give examples of other *ow* words. Use a phoneme grid to help them to build the words by adding letters before and after *ow* (see **Notes on the activities**, page 7).

Developing Literacy
Phonics
Book 3
© A & C BLACK

Ouch!

- **Join two, three or four roses to make** ⬚ou⬚ **words.**
- **Write the words.**
- **Read the words.**

In these words ⬚ou⬚ says ⬚ow⬚.

ouch!

n

ou

n

d

_____

f

ou

ch

t

_____

sh

s

n

r

_____

c

l

ou

d

_____

p

r

ou

_____

_____

- **Write three** ⬚ou⬚ **words that rhyme with** ⬚ou⬚ ⬚ch⬚ **.**

NOW try this!

Teachers' note Remind the children of their previous learning about the *ow* phoneme. Do they know another way of spelling it? Use familiar words as examples: *loud*, *cloud*, *round*. The children could contribute to a phoneme grid for building the words by adding letters before and after *ou* (see **Notes on the activities**, page 7).

Developing Literacy
Phonics
Book 3
© A & C BLACK

40

Yoyos

The mixed-up words end in $\boxed{o}$.

- **Write the words.**

- **Read the words.**

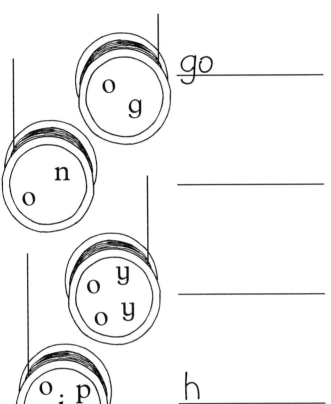

go _____

_____

_____

h _____

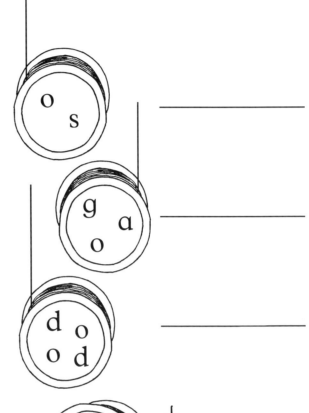

_____

_____

_____

t _____

A few words end in $\boxed{oe}$.

- **Write the words.**

h $\boxed{}$ J $\boxed{}$ f $\boxed{}$ w $\boxed{}$

- **Complete these words with $\boxed{o}$ or $\boxed{oe}$.**

ech $\boxed{}$ t $\boxed{}$ s   zer $\boxed{}$

Dictionary

- **Read the words.**

Teachers' note Write up *go* and ask the children if they can think of other short words that rhyme with it: *no, so.* (Note that *do* and *to* have the same ending but a different sound.) The children will know that the letter *o* can stand for the short *o* phoneme (for example, *hot, log, pod*). Tell them that *o* at the end of a word says its name. Encourage them to use plastic, card or wooden letters to sort out the mixed-up words.

**Developing Literacy
Phonics
Book 3
© A & C BLACK**

Glow-worms

- **Use the letters on the stones to write the** ow **words.**

- **Read the words.**

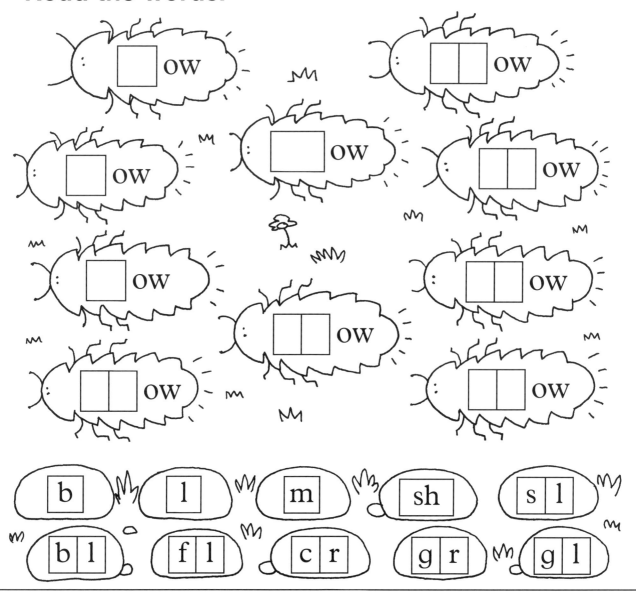

- **Re-write these mixed-up** ow **words:**

| ow | e | l | b |

| ow | y | e | ll |

| ow | a | rr |

- **Read the words.**

Teachers' note Remind the children of their previous work on the *ow* phoneme and grapheme in *cow*. Tell them that the letters *ow* can also stand for the *oe* phoneme (the name of the letter *o*). Some children might be able to identify a word on this page that can also be pronounced to rhyme with *cow*, but then has a different meaning (*bow*).

**Developing Literacy
Phonics
Book 3
© A & C BLACK**

42

Pies in the sky

- **Fill the gaps with** | ie | **or** | y |.
- **Read the words.**

p | |

cr | |

sk | |

m | |

fl | |

b | |

l | |

dr | |

fr | |

wh | |

tr | |

sp | |

d | |

sh | |

- **Complete these** | ie | **and** | y | **words:**

fl | |s   dr | |d   sl | |

pigst | | cr | |s

Now try this!

Teachers' note You could introduce this through the saying *pie in the sky*. Explain its meaning (ideas that cannot easily be carried out). Write up the saying and ask the children what they notice about the spellings of the *ie* phoneme. Encourage them to use a mini-whiteboard to try different spellings of this phoneme in the words on the pies and to decide which they think is right.

**Developing Literacy
Phonics
Book 3
© A & C BLACK**

43

High and dry

igh sounds like y in dry.

- **Circle** igh **in red.**

- **Write four other** igh **words.**
- **Read the words.**

Teachers' note Point out the title and help the children to read it. Ask them which phoneme this page is about and what they know about the letters that stand for it. They could give examples spelled *i-e* (*bike*, *life*, *ride*) and *y* (*cry*, *dry*, *fly*). Point out *high* and tell them that the letters *igh* are used together to write the same phoneme. Give examples: *fight*, *light*, *might*, *sigh*. Ask them to look carefully at the spellings as they read.

Developing Literacy
Phonics
Book 3
© A & C BLACK

Mrs Lear's ears

- **Read the rhyme.**
- **Write the missing** ear words.

"What's that I _____
with my little _____?"
said Mrs _____ to Mr _____.

"Oh _____!" said Mr _____.
"A broken _____
is what I _____."

"We're miles from home –
it isn't _____,"
said Mrs _____ as she
shed a _____.

- **Write** ear **words that mean:**
  - **easy to see**
  - **come into sight**
  - **dull.**

Look at the clues.

c	l	
a	pp	
d	r		y

Teachers' note Tell the children that they are going to read a silly rhyme called *Mrs Lear's ears*. Ask them to give examples of words that rhyme with *ear*. Point out that in most of them the *ear* phoneme is spelled *ear* (*here*, and a few other words, are exceptions). Invite volunteers to read aloud the words in the word bank: these should be used to fill the gaps (they can be used more than once).

Developing Literacy
Phonics
Book 3
© A & C BLACK

45

Pieces of eight

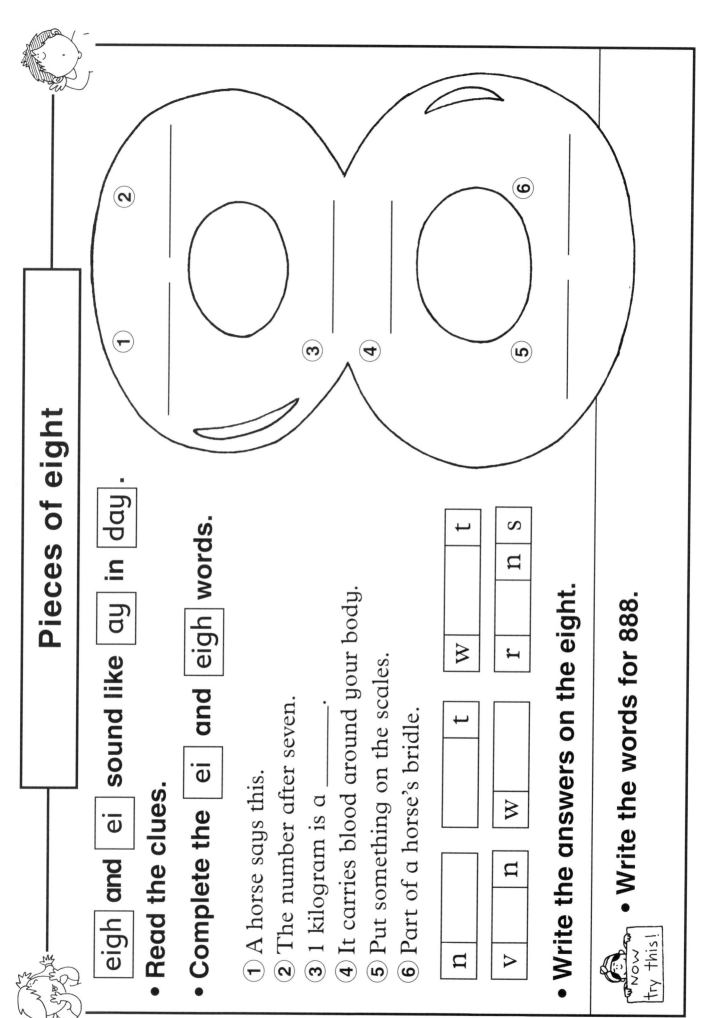

eigh and ei sound like ay in day .

- **Read the clues.**

- **Complete the ei and eigh words.**

1 A horse says this.

2 The number after seven.

3 1 kilogram is a _____ .

4 It carries blood around your body.

5 Put something on the scales.

6 Part of a horse's bridle.

n			t
		t	w

| v | n | w | |
| r | | n | s |

- **Write the answers on the eight.**

- **Write the words for 888.**

Teachers' note Hold up a number 8 and ask the children what is the first phoneme. Ask them which letters can be used to spell the phoneme *ae*, which sounds like the name of the letter *a* (*a-e*, *ai*, *ay*). Ask for examples: *take*, *pain*, *say*. Tell them that in a few words this phoneme can be spelled *eigh* or *ei* and help them to use a phoneme grid to write *eight* and then *veil*.

Developing Literacy
Phonics
Book 3
© A & C BLACK

Airy fairy

- **Write the missing letters in the** | air | **words.**

- **Read the words.**

ch

t

s

p

h

l

y

f

Find the letters on my wings.

☐ air

☐ air

☐ air

☐ air

☐ air

☐ air ☐

☐ air ☐

☐ ☐ air s

u n ☐ air

- **Write the** | air | **words.**

Now try this!

☐☐☐☐ air

☐☐☐☐ air

Teachers' note Use a jingle such as *There's a chair there. Where's the chair? Up in the air – over there in the air.* Ask the children to identify (in speech) the main phoneme. Write *air* and tell them that they are going to learn other words that contain the letters *air* standing for the phoneme *air*. Model how to complete the first word using *p, h, l, f* or *ch*.

**Developing Literacy
Phonics
Book 3
© A & C BLACK**

A fair share

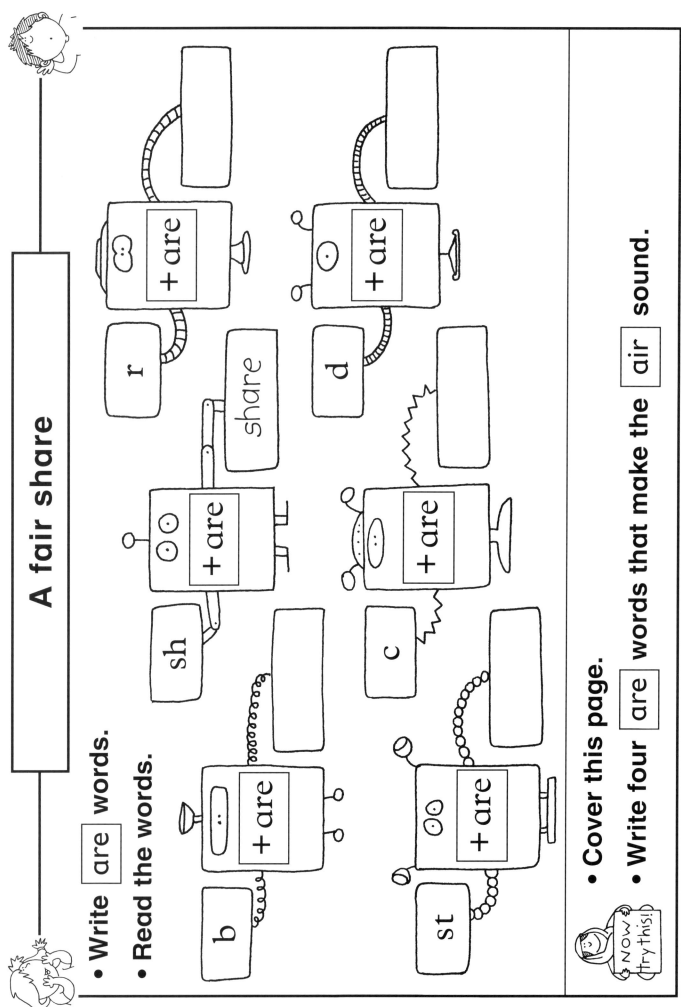

- **Write** `are` **words.**
- **Read the words.**

r + `are`

share

sh + `are`

d + `are`

c + `are`

b + `are`

st + `are`

- **Cover this page.**
- **Write four** `are` **words that make the** `air` **sound.**

NOW try this!

Teachers' note Remind the children of their previous learning about the phoneme *air*. Write up the letters *are* and tell them that this letter combination, too, can stand for the same phoneme. Give them some examples. You could arrange these in sentences: *A bare mare is very rare. Don't stare at a bare mare. Show you care – share the fare.*

**Developing Literacy
Phonics
Book 3
© A & C BLACK**

Word turns

er , or and ur can all say ur .

• **Spin a beginning.**

• **Spin an ending.**

 Dictionary

• **Write the** er , or **or** ur **words on the grids.**

• **Read the words.**

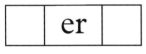
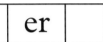
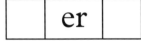
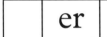

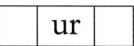

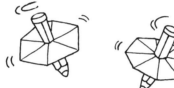

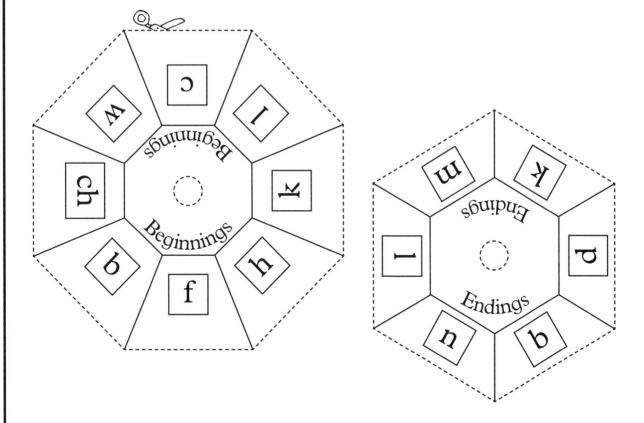

Teachers' note This practises the *er*, *or* and *ur* spellings of the *ur* phoneme. Copy the spinners onto thin card. Cut them out and push a small pencil through the hole. The children spin a beginning and write it on a mini-whiteboard. They add *er*, *or* or *ur* and then spin an ending. Have they made a real word? Allow them three tries. Use a dictionary to check.

Developing Literacy
Phonics
Book 3
© A & C BLACK

Chirping birds

- **Finish the** ir **words on the birds.**

- **Read the words.**

s[ ]

g[ ]l

b[ ]d

f[ ]st

d[ ]t

f[ ]m

tw[ ]l

sk[ ]t

c[ ]cle

c[ ]cus

- **Write two other** ir **words.**

Now try this!

30

th[ ][ ][ ]

th[ ][ ][ ][ ]

Teachers' note Remind the children of their previous learning about the *er, or* and *ur* spellings of the *ur* vowel phoneme before introducing the *ir* spelling and giving examples. Other useful words include *dirty, girder, squirm, squirt, swirl, third, thirst*. The children could make up some 'bird songs' with the words they have created.

Developing Literacy
Phonics
Book 3
© A & C BLACK

Pears or pearls?

In these words ear sounds like pear or pearl .

- **Read the clues.**

- **Write the answers on the pears or the pearls.**

- **Read the words.**

Clues

A fruit.

The planet we live on.

Not late.

An animal.

A jewel.

You do this at school.

You ____ clothes.

Rip apart.

Answers

bear	early
Earth	learn
pear	pearl
tear	wear

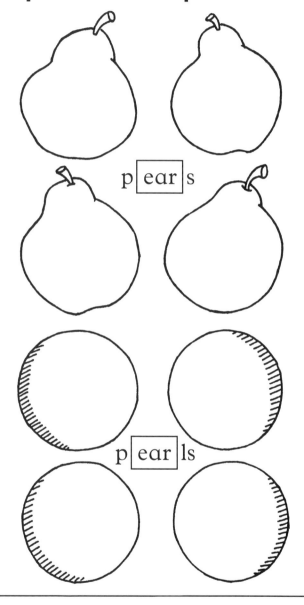

p ear s

p ear ls

- **Cover this page.**

- **Write two words that sound like pear .**

- **Write two words that sound like pearl .**

Teachers' note Remind the children of their previous learning about the different spellings of the vowel phonemes *air* and *ur* (see pages 47–50) before introducing the *ear* spelling for both phonemes and giving examples: *air – bear, pear, tear, wear*; *ur – early, Earth, learn, pearl*. Other useful *ear* words with the *ur* sound include *earn, heard, search*. Regional pronunciations may vary.

Developing Literacy
Phonics
Book 3
© A & C BLACK

Corks and forks

- **Write the** `or` **words.**
- **Read the words.**

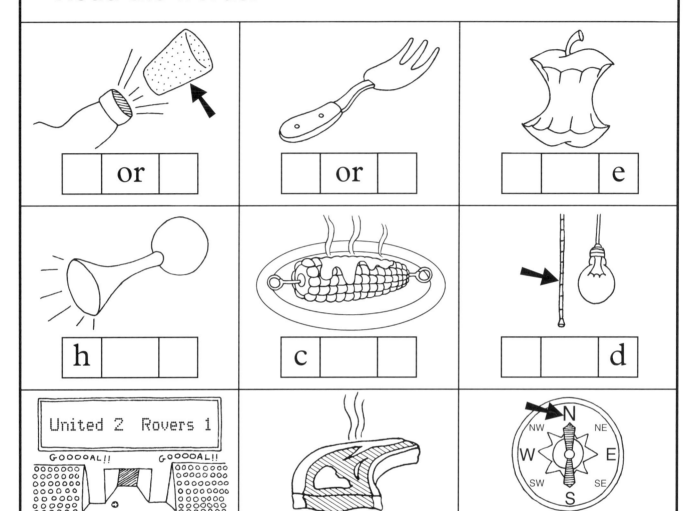

☐ **or** ☐	☐ **or** ☐	☐ ☐ **e**
h ☐ ☐	**c** ☐ ☐ ☐	☐ ☐ **d**
s c ☐ ☐	**p** ☐ ☐ ☐	**n** ☐ ☐

- **Write the** `or` **words.**

Your birthday is the date you were ☐ **or** ☐ .

I've got a ☐ **or** ☐ throat.

The early part of the day is the ☐ **or** ☐ ☐ .

A town next to the sea is called a ☐ **or** ☐ .

Teachers' note Write up *or* and ask the children if they know what it says. Remind them of their previous learning about *or* saying *ur*, as in *word* and *work* (see page 49). Write *or* on a phoneme grid and tell them that more commonly *or* says *au*. Ask the children to add other phonemes before and after it to create words: *for*, *form*, *fort*, *more*, *sore*, *sort*, *tore*, *torn*, *wore*, *worn*.

Developing Literacy
Phonics
Book 3
© A & C BLACK

A pure cure

- **Read the clues.**

- **Write the** ⃞ur⃞ **words.**

The doctor will

_____ you.

I am painting a

_____.

This means very clean. _____

This is the name of a planet. _____

_____ means more than one.

- **Write** ⃞ur⃞ **words that mean:**

  – **great anger**

  – **in court they say**
  'guilty' or 'not guilty'.

These both
end in ⃞y⃞.

Now try this!

Teachers' note Start by reading the words in the word bank together. Encourage the children to tackle the longer words by splitting them up into phonemes, for example, *p-l-ure-a-l* and *Ure-a-n-er-s*. Point out the new vowel phoneme *ure* in each word and help the children to pronounce it correctly. Make sure they understand the meaning of all the word bank words before they start the activity.

Developing Literacy
Phonics
Book 3
© A & C BLACK

Choose and chews

The missing phonemes all sound the same.

- Write ew , oo , u or ue .
- Read the words.

Dictionary

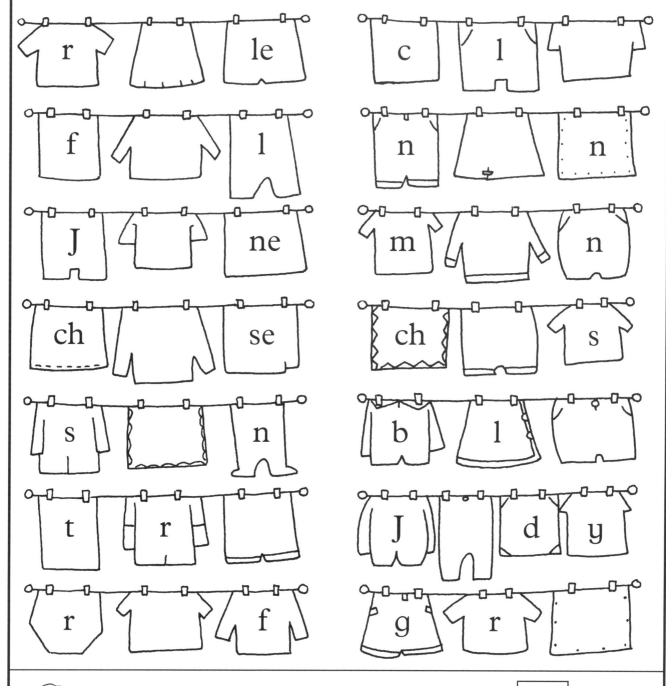

r   le   c   l

f   l   n   n

J   ne   m   n

ch   se   ch   s

s   n   b   l

t   r   J   d   y

r   f   g   r

NOW try this!

- Write a silly rhyme using your ew , oo , u and ue words.

Teachers' note Remind the children of their previous learning about long vowel phonemes. Write up some examples with *u*: *prune*, *rude*. Ask a volunteer to write *blue* on a phoneme grid. Which letters stand for the *ue* phoneme? Ask the others to use this to help them to spell *glue* and *true*. Ask if they can hear the same sound in *choose* and *boot* and in *chews* and *grew*. Write these words on grids and point out the different spellings.

Developing Literacy
Phonics
Book 3
© A & C BLACK

Thanks for this

Choose the correct card.

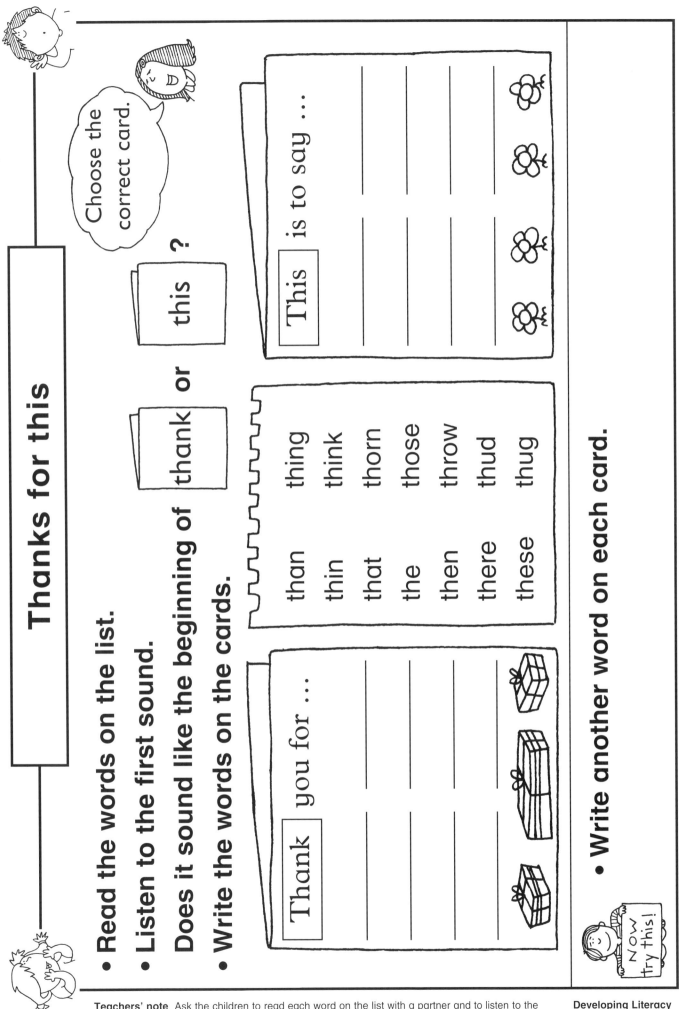

thank **or** this **?**

thing   than
think   thin
thorn   that
those   the
throw   then
thud   there
thug   these

This is to say …

Thank you for …

- **Read the words on the list.**
- **Listen to the first sound.**
- **Does it sound like the beginning of** thank **or** this**?**
- **Write the words on the cards.**
- **Write another word on each card.**

Now try this!

Teachers' note Ask the children to read each word on the list with a partner and to listen to the sound made by the letters *th*. Is it like the first sound of *thank* or *this*? Emphasise the *th* phonemes as you say the words. Possible words for the extension activity include *their*, *them*, *they*; *thirty*, *thistle*, *three*, *thumb*, *thunder*.

Developing Literacy
Phonics
Book 3
© A & C BLACK

Hard or soft c

- **Write** c **in the gaps.**
- **Read the words.**
- **Write them on the caterpillar or the centipede.**

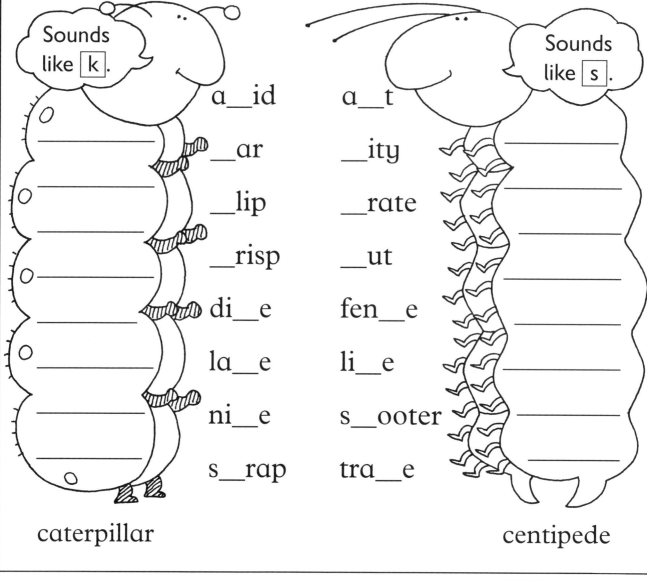

Sounds like k.

a__id

__ar

__lip

__risp

di__e

la__e

ni__e

s__rap

caterpillar

Sounds like s.

a__t

__ity

__rate

__ut

fen__e

li__e

s__ooter

tra__e

centipede

Now try this!

- **Read the words.**
- **Listen to the** c.
- **Write** k **or** s.

creep ☐

parcel ☐

price ☐

tractor ☐

Teachers' note Write up *c* and ask the children which phoneme it stands for. Draw out that it can say *k* or *s*. Remind them about the terms *hard* and *soft* for these phonemes. Write up some examples and ask the children to say whether the *c* is hard or soft: *ace, cat, price, scream*. Draw attention to the letters following the letter *c*: which letters usually make the *c* hard? Which ones usually make it soft?

Developing Literacy
Phonics
Book 3
© A & C BLACK

Hard or soft g

- **Write** g **in the gaps.**
- **Read the words.**
- **Write them on the giraffe or the gorilla.**

Sounds like j.

Sounds like g.

an__el

pe__

__ate

__in__er

__rab

hin__e

ma__ic

sta__

bar__e

__as

__em

__oal

__ulp

hu__e

ra__e

bra__

giraffe

gorilla

Now try this!

- **Read the words.**
- **Listen to the** g **.**
- **Write** j **or** g **.**

gold ☐

giant ☐

large ☐

grip ☐

Teachers' note Write up *g* and ask the children which phoneme it stands for. Draw out that it can say *g* or *j*. Remind them about the terms *hard* and *soft* for these phonemes. Write up some examples and ask the children to say whether the *g* is hard or soft: *age, glad, goat, page*. Draw attention to the letters following the letter *g*: which letters usually make the *g* hard? Which ones usually make it soft?

Developing Literacy
Phonics
Book 3
© A & C BLACK

Say the $\boxed{k}$

- **Read the words.**

  Do we say the $\boxed{k}$ or keep it silent?

- **Write the words on the correct list.**

keep	kit	king	knot
knee	knit	knickers	know
kerb	kite	knuckle	kind
kneel	kiss	kick	knock

Say the $\boxed{k}$.

Keep the $\boxed{k}$ silent.

- **Write another word on each list.**

Clues:

Teachers' note Write up *k* and ask the children to say the sound it makes. Ask them for examples of words containing the letter *k*. Write up the word *knee* and help them to read it. What do they notice about the *k*? Remind them of their previous work on 'silent *k*' and ask them to read the words with a partner and to decide whether the *k* is said or is silent.

Developing Literacy
Phonics
Book 3
© A & C BLACK

Hear the g

- **Say the words.**

  Do we hear the g or is it silent?

- **Write the words under the goat or the gnu.**

game	gnaw
goat	gnu
gnarled	gas
give	gnome
gnash	gum

We hear the g.

goat

gnu

The g is silent.

- **Write another word in each set.**

Clues:

Teachers' note Write up *g* and ask the children to say the sound it makes. Ask them for examples of words containing the letter *g*. Write up the word *gnat* and help them to read it. What do they notice about the *g*? Remind them of their previous work on 'silent *g*' and ask them to read the words with a partner and to decide whether the *g* can be heard or is silent.

Developing Literacy
Phonics
Book 3
© A & C BLACK

Beans on bread

- **Read the** ☐ea **words.**

- **Listen to the sound that** ☐ea **makes.**

- **Write the words on the beans or the bread.**

please   deaf   leaf   beach

tea   death

jeans   meadow   seal   heaven   ahead   seat

weapon   instead   cream   season

already   breath   breathe   sweat

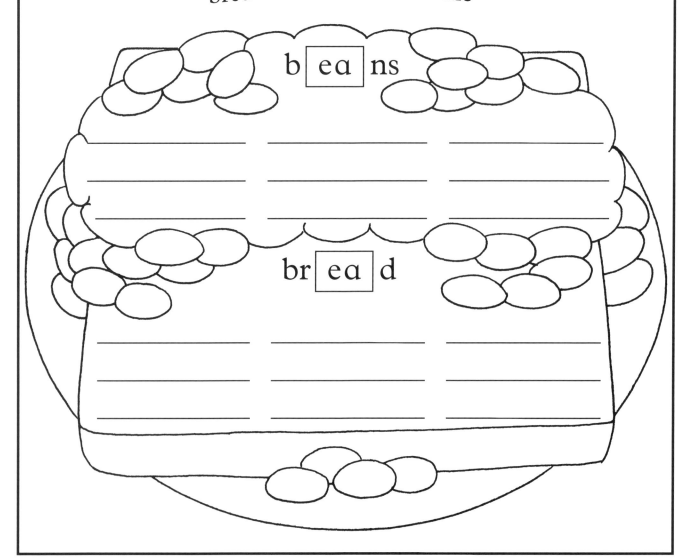

Teachers' note Write up *ea* and ask the children to say the sound it makes. Write up some examples of words containing the letters *ea*: *dead, deaf, eat, cream*. Remind them that *ea* can stand for *e* or *ee* (it can be short or long). Ask them to read the words with a partner and to decide whether the *ea* makes a short or a long sound in each case.

Developing Literacy
Phonics
Book 3
© A & C BLACK

Hares and chairs

- **Read the words in the word bank.**

- **Look for** │are│ **or** │air│ .

- **Write them on the hares or the chairs.**

Word bank

air	beware	dairy	dare
fair	fairy	glare	hair
mare	pair	scare	share

h │are│ s

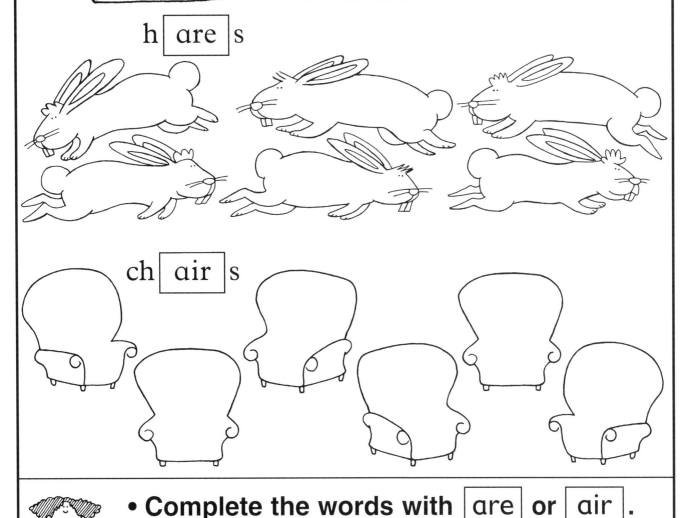

ch │air│ s

- **Complete the words with** │are│ **or** │air│ .

squ□□□   st□□□case   r□□□

Teachers' note Read the page title with the children and draw attention to *hare*. They should know another spelling of a word that sounds the same (*hair*). Explain *hare* if necessary. Compare the two spellings of the *air* phoneme and ask the children to look at the spellings of the words as they read them. They could also work in pairs with one reading the words and the other writing them without looking at the page.

Developing Literacy
Phonics
Book 3
© A & C BLACK

Short straws

• **Write** [or] **or** [aw] **in the gaps.**

Dictionary

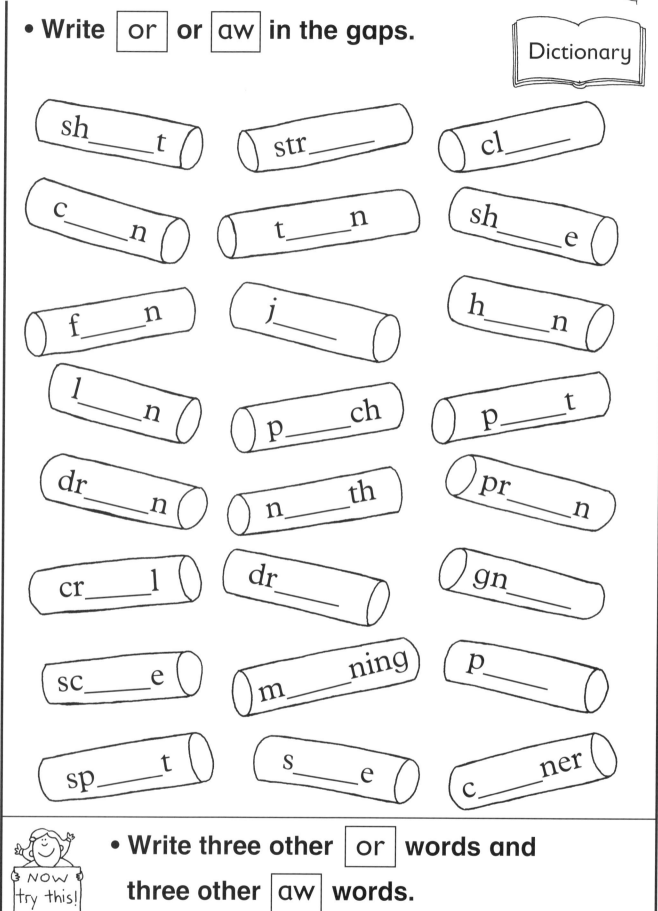

sh___t   str_____   cl_____

c___n   t___n   sh___e

f___n   j_____   h___n

l___n   p___ch   p___t

dr___n   n___th   pr___n

cr___l   dr_____   gn_____

sc___e   m___ning   p_____

sp___t   s___e   c___ner

• **Write three other** [or] **words and three other** [aw] **words.**

NOW try this!

Teachers' note The children could try writing these words on a mini-whiteboard using both spellings of the *au* phoneme in turn. Ask them to decide which is right, using a dictionary where possible. Some might need adult help.

Developing Literacy
Phonics
Book 3
© A & C BLACK

Fill the gap: er , ir , ur

- **Fill the gaps with** er , ir **or** ur .
- **Read the words.**

Dictionary

 f ☐ n	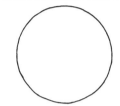 c ☐ cle	 g ☐ l
 ch ☐ ch	 b ☐ ger	 iceb ☐ g
 th ☐ ty	 m ☐ maid	 t ☐ nip
 b ☐ ner	 h ☐ bs	 th ☐ teen

Now try this!

- **Cover this page.**
- **Write two** er **words, two** ir **words and two** ur **words.**

Teachers' note The children could try writing these words on a mini-whiteboard using all three spellings of the *ur* phoneme in turn. Ask them to decide which is right, using a dictionary where possible. Some of them might need adult help.

Developing Literacy Phonics Book 3 © A & C BLACK

Phantom phonemes

- **Choose middle letters to make real words.**

- **Read the words.**

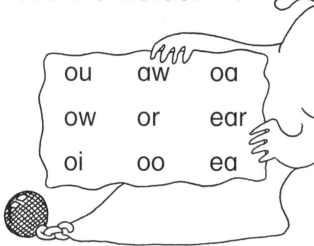

ou	aw	oa
ow	or	ear
oi	oo	ea

Choose from my list.

h___l   b___l   l___d

cr___l   b___d   cr___n

dr___n   sp___n   m___n

cl___d   c___ner   cl___k

p___nt   cl___n   r___nd

Now try this!

- **Change the middles of four of the words.**

- **Write the new words.**

Teachers' note This is an open-ended activity in which different words could be correct. Ask the children to try different vowels in each gap until they find a set that sounds right. Remind them about the different phonemes each group of vowels can stand for.

Developing Literacy
Phonics
Book 3
© A & C BLACK